THIS BOOK
BELONGS TO

....

To mums and dads,
especially George and Nancy, Meg and Stan

Other books by Nick Butterworth and Mick Inkpen:

THE SCHOOL TRIP
THE SPORTS DAY
JUST LIKE JASPER!
JASPER'S BEANSTALK

Copyright © Nick Butterworth and Mick Inkpen 1985

The right of Nick Butterworth and Mick Inkpen to be identified as
the author and the illustrator of this Work has been asserted by them
in accordance with the Copyright, Designs and Patents Act 1988.

First published 1985 by Hodder and Stoughton.
This edition published in 2005 by Hodder Children's Books
338 Euston Road
London NW1 3BH
Hodder Children's Books Australia
Level 17/207 Kent Street
Sydney, NSW 2000

30 29 28 27 26 25

A catalogue record of this book is available from the British Library

ISBN 978 0 340 39894 4

Printed and bound in Hong Kong

Hodder Children's Books is a division of Hachette Children's Books

An Hachette UK Company

www.hachette.co.uk

THE
NATIVITY PLAY

NICK BUTTERWORTH
AND
MICK INKPEN

Hodder
Children's
Books

A division of Hachette Children's Books

Tracy and Sam are in their school nativity play.
Their mum is helping with the costumes.
Tracy is one of the angels. She feels beautiful in her
golden halo. She wants a magic wand.
But mum says that angels don't have magic wands.

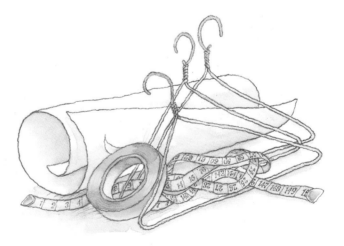

Sam is a shepherd. With enough stripy towels
he'll look just like the real thing.
Mum is having trouble with his beard. It's made
of wool and Sellotape, but it won't stay on.
Sam is practising his words. 'The Saviour of
the world is born, the Saviour of the world is
born,' he says to himself.
'Don't worry,' says mum. 'It'll be all right on
the night.'

At last everything is ready.
The audience are in their seats. Mum and dad are
sitting in the front row with Mrs Booth from next door.
Backstage, everyone is feeling nervous.
'Now,' says Miss Harvey, 'nice and loud everybody.
And shepherds, don't stand in front of Mary.'

The curtain opens.
'InthedaysofCaesarAugustus . . .'
'Slow down a bit, Katie,' whispers Miss Harvey.
'Joseph, the carpenter, and his wife, Mary, went
up to Bethlehem . . .'

Joseph looks for somewhere to stay.
'No room,' says the first innkeeper.
'Full up,' says the second innkeeper.
'Too late,' says the third innkeeper.
'But I am worried about my wife. She is
having a baby,' says Joseph with a grin.
The third innkeeper has an idea.
'I have a stable you can use,' he says.

'And so Mary's baby, Jesus, was born in a stable.'
The animals gather round the baby. They begin
to sing.
'Away in a manger, no crib for a bed,
The little Lord Jesus lay down his sweet head . . .'
'Sing up,' says Miss Harvey.

Here come the shepherds! But where's Sam?
Ah – it's alright. He was in the toilet.
Tracy, the beautiful angel, stands in front of them.
'Fear not!' she shouts. 'I bring you tidings of great joy.'
She tells the shepherds
all about the baby Jesus.
The other angels play
their recorders.

'Come, let us go over to Bethlehem,' say the
shepherds.
They gather round to look at the baby.
One of the shepherds is looking at the audience.
He waves. 'Hello Dad.'

Now comes Sam's big moment. He walks to
the front. His voice is clear and loud.
'The Saviour of the world is born,' he tells
the audience.
'Lovely,' says Mrs Booth.

There is a noise at the back of the hall.
Wise men are coming from the east. But the
door won't open.
One of the dads lets them in.
Slowly, they walk up to the stage. The wise men
look serious.
Their camel is having trouble climbing the steps.

'Where is he who is born to be king?
For we have seen his star in the east and have
come to worship him,' says the wise man
with the bath salts. Joseph points.
The wise men lay their gifts by the manger.
'Gold I give to the infant king.'
'Frankincense the gift I bring,'
'Myrrh is mine, so let us sing,
Our joyful Christmas praises ring . . .'

So Joseph and Mary, the innkeepers,
the shepherds, the angels, the wise men,
the camel, the donkey, the sheep and the cow
all sing together.
'Join in, everybody,' says Miss Harvey.
Mr Bryant, the caretaker, switches on the
overhead projector and up come the words.

Hark! the herald-angels sing,
Glory to the new-born King,
Peace on earth, and mercy mild,
God and sinners reconciled.
Joyful, all ye nations, rise,
Join the triumph of the skies;
With the angelic host proclaim,
'Christ is born in Bethlehem.'